Great **Bands** of the **60s**

Exclusive Distributors:
Music Sales Limited
8-9 Frith Street,
London W1V 5TZ, England.
Music Sales Pty Limited
120 Rothschild Avenue,
Rosebery, NSW 2018,
Australia.

Order No. AM952347
ISBN 0-7119-7315-6

Designed by Pearce Marchbank, Studio Twenty
Printed in the United Kingdom by Caligraving Limited, Thetford, Norfolk.

Your Guarantee of Quality
As publishers, we strive to produce every book to the highest commercial standards.
This book has been carefully designed to minimise awkward page turns and to make playing from it a real pleasure. Particular care has been given to specifying acid-free, neutral-sized paper made from pulps which have not been elemental chlorine bleached. This pulp is from farmed sustainable forests and was produced with special regard for the environment.
Throughout, the printing and binding have been planned to ensure a sturdy, attractive publication which should give years of enjoyment.
If your copy fails to meet our high standards, please inform us and we will gladly replace it.

Music Sales' complete catalogue describes thousands of titles and is available in full colour sections by subject, direct from Music Sales Limited. Please state your areas of interest and send a cheque/postal order for £1.50 for postage to: Music Sales Limited, Newmarket Road, Bury St. Edmunds, Suffolk IP33 3YB.

Wise Publications
London/New York/Paris/Sydney/Copenhagen/Madrid

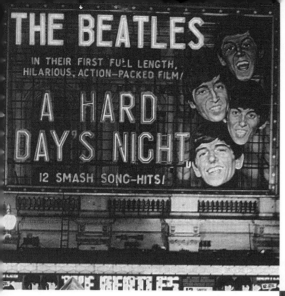

They say if you can remember the sixties you weren't there, so here's a quick refresher. As the rock 'n' roll upsurge of the fifties solidified into modern pop music as we know it, we were left with a decade of huge innovation and texture, a high watermark in contemporary art. As society threw off the shackles of post-war austerity, young people discovered their own culture and identity, and pop musicians were recast as spokespersons and activists rather than simple idols.

A Hard Day's Night was the most iconic and fully-formed of the early Beatles' singles, with its irresistible mix of R&B riffing and pop libido. The title was taken from a comment made by Ringo after a day on the set of The Beatles'

first film - which eventually shared the same title. By 1964, the Fab Four were spearheading what was christened the British Invasion, as UK beat groups shook American teenagers out of daydreams about squeaky-clean crooners in favour of a more visceral breed of pop star.

The British Invasion is also represented by fellow Liverpudlians Gerry & The Pacemakers, who recorded You'll Never Walk Alone from Rogers and Hammerstein's *Carousel*, ultimately turning the song into a football terrace anthem. The London-based Kinks, also at the forefront of the new music were led by Ray Davies, whose All Day And All Of The Night remains arguably the defining pop song of the decade. Despite two of the group professing a dislike of pop music, Manfred Mann racked up some sixteen British hit singles in the sixties, and among the most memorable was Pretty Flamingo.

After the British Invasion subsided, musicians used the decade to explore new musical avenues, harnessing the rapid advances in recording technology now available to them. Song structures quickly evolved from a base R&B template, a shift complemented by the increasing popularity of the long playing record. The best examples include Procol Harum's A Whiter Shade Of Pale, an inimitable slice of psychedelic whimsy. With Bach's 'Suite No.3 in D Major' serving as inspiration, and surreal, reflective lyrics, it perfectly captured 1967's Summer of Love mood. From the same year came Pink

Floyd's incandescent and English-to-the-core See Emily Play, Syd Barrett's finest recorded moment. From the Moody Blues, who had tried their hand at the 'beat combo' game, came the romantic melodrama of Nights In White Satin, a song which defied previous pop conventions and expectations.

Then there was the American West Coast sound, represented here by The Mamas and The Papas (though they were actually a product of the Greenwich Village folk community in New York). California Dreaming became an anthem at Haight-Ashbury love-ins, and from 1967 to 1968 The Mamas and The Papas were the hippy movement's indispensable component. Also

rooted in the folk tradition were The Byrds. Eight Miles High, which originally faced a radio ban because of its assumed drug references - was taken from one of the decade's most fascinating albums, *Fifth Dimension*.

There was also a huge British blues boom, as rock musicians retreated to the rudimentary three-chord framework of popular music's originators for inspiration, before taking off in spectacular flights of improvisation. In this no-one surpassed the legendary Cream, sampled here with Sunshine Of Your Love, one of several tracks that persuaded devotees to tout the slogan 'Clapton Is God' to anyone who would listen. The Animals' House Of The Rising Sun, similarly, brought new lustre to old moves. But if anyone was possessed by the spirit of Robert Johnson, that honour befell Jimi Hendrix, whose awesome version of Bob Dylan's All Along The Watchtower broke him in America.

We've also found room for those unlikely stars of the sixties, The Troggs, whose eventual self-destruction became one of the legends of the decade (before Love Is All Around was resurrected when it was featured on the soundtrack of *Four Weddings And A Funeral*). Something In The Air, recorded by Thunderclap Newman, was almost the epitome of the London Tin Pan Alley scene of the late 1960s. The band's line-up included the eccentric singer/songwriter Speedy Keene and a fourteen year old guitarist named

Jimmy McCulloch, the latter of whom later went on to play with Stone The Crows and, most notably, Paul McCartney's Wings. After the huge success of this song, which was a No. 1 hit in the summer of '69, Thunderclap Newman were never heard of again.

The Bee Gees' sublime New York Mining Disaster 1941 is as far removed from their tenure as seventies disco dollies as it is possible to imagine, and argues for a reappraisal of their talents. Conversely, some of the staples of the sixties seemed to belong to a different period entirely; for example The Righteous Brothers' Unchained Melody (credit Phil Spector's production of the fifties chestnut) and the Spencer Davis Group's Keep On Running. So too The Everly Brothers' When Will I Be Loved, three songs that sprang from an altogether more innocent wellspring, when pop observed the rules of adolescent engagement. That can hardly be said of Steppenwolf, whose Born To Be Wild (taken from the soundtrack to biker classic *Easy Rider*) no doubt drove fraught parents to distraction with its advocacy of hell-raising lawlessness.

The Who's My Generation struck a similar chord, although Pete Townshend and company were even more direct in underscoring the generational divide. Those other upstarts, The Rolling Stones, implored us to Not Fade Away, which was actually a cover of a Buddy Holly song rather than a nod to the 'die young, stay pretty' ethos. It brought them their first Top 10 hit. Both The Who and The Stones would become stalwarts of the next two decades of music, prospering as they progressed as writers and musicians. Many of the others did indeed 'fade away' to piecemeal solo careers or the revival circuit, but not without leaving an indelible imprint on the history of popular music. Compositions such as those included here remain widely acknowledged by modern musicians as the true benchmark of pop songwriting. *Alex Ogg*

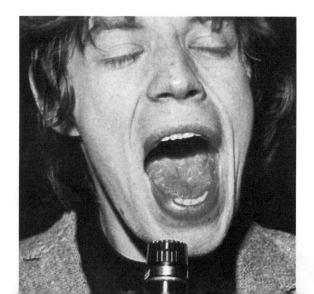

California Dreaming

Words & Music by John Phillips

6

7

All Along The Watchtower

Words & Music by Bob Dylan

All Day And All Of The Night

Words & Music by Ray Davies

1. I'm not con-tent to be with you in the day—
(Verses 2 & 3 see block lyrics)

—— time.

Girl, I want to

be with you all of the_____ time.   The

on - ly time I feel al - right_____ is by your_____ side._____

_____   Girl I want to be with you all of the_____

_____ time, all day and all of the night.   All day and

all of the night.

All day and all of the night.

(Oh, get 'em all out.)

Guitar solo

cont. ad lib.

Verses 2 & 3:
I believe that you and me'll last forever
Oh yeah, all day and night I'm yours, leave me never.

The only time I feel alright *etc.*

Born To Be Wild

Words & Music by Mars Bonfire

1. Get your mo-tor run-ning,— head out on the high-way,
(Verses 2 & 3 see block lyric)

look-ing for ad-ven-ture, in what-

-ev - er comes our way._____ Yeah dar - lin' gon - na

make it hap - pen, take the world in a love em - brace,—

fire all of your guns_____ at once_____ and

ex - plode in - to space._____

Verse 2:
I like smoke and lightning
Heavy metal thunder
Racing in the wind
And the feeling that I'm under.

Yeah darlin' *etc.*

Verse 3: (𝄋.) — as Verse 1

Eight Miles High

Words & Music by Gene Clark, Jim McGuinn & David Crosby

Verse 2:
Nowhere is there warmth to be found
Among those afraid of losing their ground
Rain grey town known for its sound
In places small faces unbound.

Verse 3:
Round the squares huddled in storms
Some laughing, some just shapeless forms
Sidewalk scenes and black limousines
Some living, some standing alone.

A Hard Day's Night

Words & Music by John Lennon & Paul McCartney

get home to you, ___ I find the things that you do ___ will make me
love to come home ___ 'Cause when I get you a - lone ___ you know I'll

feel ___ al - right. ___
be ___ O. ___ K. ___

(2) You know I ___ When I'm home ___

ev - 'ry - thing seems ___ to be al - right. When I'm home ___

feel - ing you hold - ing me tight,

25

So why I love to come home __ 'Cause when I get you a-lone __ you know I

feel __ O. __ K. __ When I'm home __ ev-'ry-thing seems __ to be al-

House Of The Rising Sun

Arranged by Alan Price

1. There is a house in New Or-leans, they call the Ris - ing

Sun. And it's been the ruin of ma-ny— a poor boy, and

God, I know— I'm one.

2. My

2. moth - er was a tai - lor sewed my new blue
3. on - ly thing a gam-bler needs is a suit - case and a

done, spend your lives—— in sin and—— mi-se-ry—— in the house—— of the Ris - ing Sun.

5. Well—— I've got

5. one foot on the plat-form—— the
6. is a house in New Or - - - leans they

Keep On Running

Words & Music by Jackie Edwards

1. Keep on run - ning, keep on hid-

(Verses 2 & 3 (𝄋) see block lyric)

(sim.)

- ing, one fine day___ I'm gon - na be the___ one

to make you un-der-stand,___ oh yeah! I'm gon-na be your___ man.___

1.

___ Keep on___ run-

2, 3.

Hey hey hey!___ Ev - 'ry-one is talk - ing a-bout___ me,

it make me feel so___ bad.___ Hey hey hey!___ Ev - 'ry-one is laugh-

Verses 2 & 3 (𝄋):
Keep on running
Running from my arms.
One fine day I'm gonna be the one
To make you understand.
Oh yeah! I'm gonna be your man.

Love Is All Around

Words & Music by Reg Presley

1. I feel it in my fin - gers, I feel it in my toes.
(Verse 2 see block lyric)

The love that's all a - round me

You know I love you, I al - ways will, my mind's made up by the

way that I feel. There's no be - gin - ning, there'll be no end, 'cause

on my love you can de - pend.

Verse 2:
I see your face before me
As I lay on my bed;
I cannot get to thinking
Of all the things you said.
You gave your promise to me
And I gave mine to you;
I need someone beside me
In everything I do.

Love Me Do

Words & Music by John Lennon & Paul McCartney

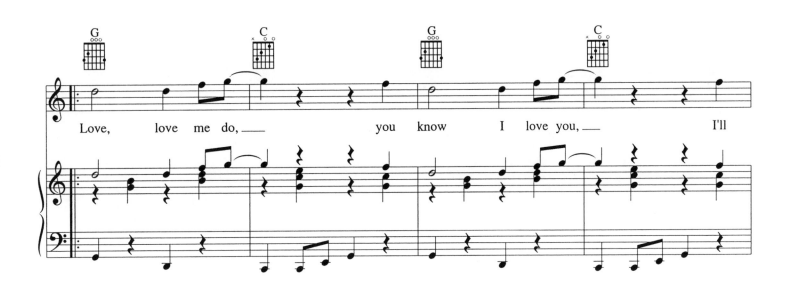

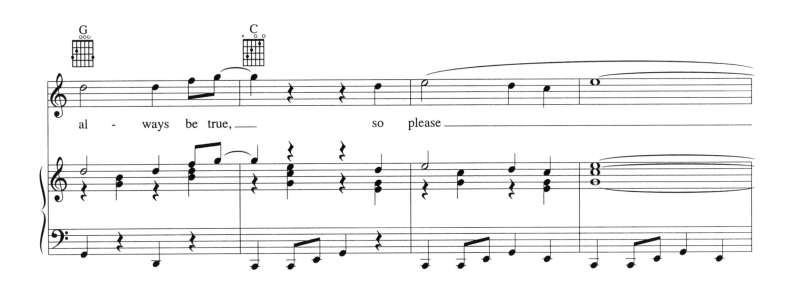

My Generation

Words & Music by Pete Townshend

not tryin' to cause a big sen-sa-tion. I'm just
[Talk-in' 'bout my gen-er-a-tion]

talk-in' 'bout my gen-er-a-tion. This is my gen-er-
[Talk-in' 'bout my gen-er-a-tion]

a-tion, This is my gen-er-a-tion, ba-by.

1.
N.C.

2.

New York Mining Disaster 1941

Words & Music by Barry Gibb & Robin Gibb

In the e - vent of some - thing hap-pen-ing to

me, there is some-thing I would like you all to see. It's just a

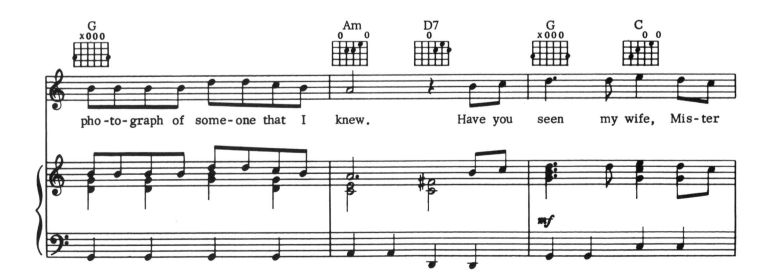

pho-to-graph of some-one that I knew. Have you seen my wife, Mis-ter

bed think - ing those who once ex - ist - ed must be dead? Have you

seen my wife, Mis - ter Jones? Do you know what it's like on the

out - side? Don't go talk - ing too loud, you'll cause a land - slide, Mis - ter

Jones. In the e -

D. S. al Coda

Coda

Jones.

Nights In White Satin

Words & Music by Justin Hayward

Nights in white sa - tin ____ nev - er reach - ing the end,
Ga - zing at peo - ple, ____ some hand in hand,

Let - ters I've writ - ten ____ nev - er mean - ing to send. ____
Just what I'm go - ing through they ____ can't un - der - stand. ____

Beau - ty I'd al - ways missed with these eyes ____ be - fore,
Some try to tell me ____ thoughts they can - not de - fend,

Not Fade Away

Words & Music by Charles Hardin & Norman Petty

love that's love__ and not fade a-way.__
for you to know__ just how I feel.__

A
A

love that's love__ and not fade a-way.__
love is real__ and not fade a-way.__

I said,

love is real__ and not fade a-way.__

To Coda ⊕

Penny Lane

Words & Music by John Lennon & Paul McCartney

There be-neath the blue ___ sub-ur-ban skies ___
There be-neath the blue ___ sub-ur-ban skies ___

___ I sit. And mean-while back in Pen-ny Lane ___ there is a fire-man with an
___ I sit. And

hour - glass, ___ And in his pock - et is a por-trait of the Queen. He likes to

keep his fire - en-gine clean; ___ It's a clean ___ ma-chine!

Pen - ny Lane ____ is in my ears ____

and in my eyes. ____ Full of fish ____

Pretty Flamingo

Words & Music by Mark Barkan

Pictures Of Lily

Words & Music by Peter Townshend

And now my nights ain't quite so lone-ly
If on-ly I'd been born in Lily's time,
In fact I—
It would have been al - right—
I don't feel bad at all——
It would have been al - right——

I don't feel bad at all——

CHORUS

Pic-tures of Li - ly made my life—— so won - der - ful——

Pic-tures of Li - ly helped—— me sleep at night——

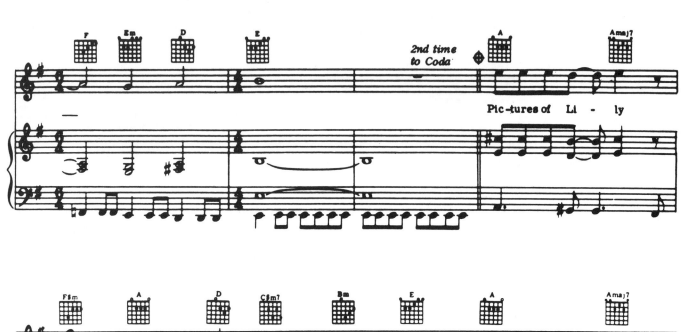

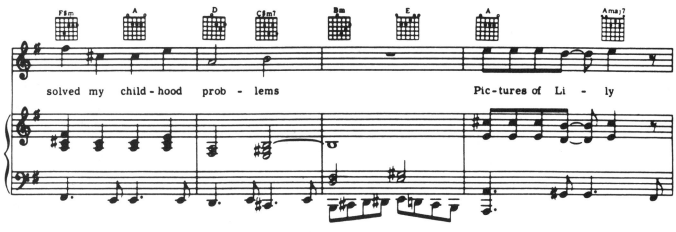

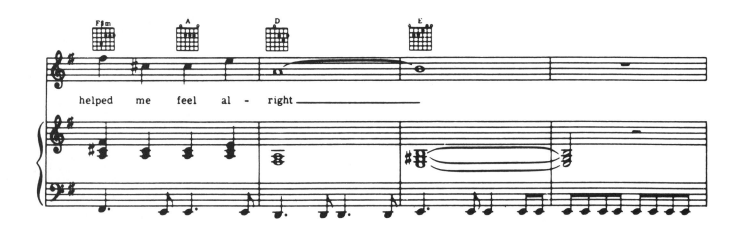

Proud Mary

Words & Music by John C. Fogerty

Moderately, with a heavy beat

Verse

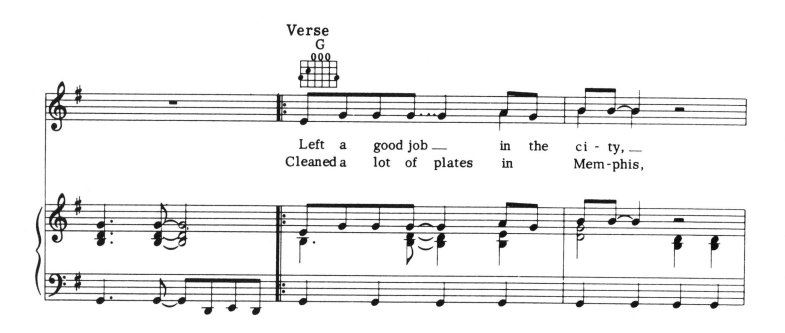

Left a good job _ in the ci - ty, _
Cleaned a lot of plates in Mem - phis,

Work- in' for The Man ev'ry night and day, _ And I ne-ver lost one min-
Pumped a lot of pain in New Or - leans, _ But I ne-ver saw the good-

Chorus

Big wheel keep on turnin', Proud Ma-ry keep on burn-in', Roll-
-in', roll-in', roll-in' on the riv-er.

Verse
G

If you come down_ to the riv-er, Bet you gon-na find some peo - ple who live._

D.S. al ⊕ 𝄋

You don't have to wor-ry_ 'cause you have no mon-ey,_ Peo-ple on the riv-er are hap-py to give._

⊕ *Coda*

G

repeat and fade

Roll-in', _ roll - in', _ roll-in' on the riv - er._____

Something In The Air

Words & Music by Speedy Keene

Call out the in-sti-ga - tors be-cause_ there's some-thing in the air,_

_____ we got to get_ to-geth - er soon-er or lat - er be-cause_ the

re-vo-lu-tion's here and you know. it's right.

And you know that— it's right. We have got to

get it to-geth-er, we have got to get it to-geth-er

now.——

Block off the streets and hous - es be-cause— there's some-thing in the air.—

We got to get— to-geth-er soon-er or lat - er be-cause— the

re - vo - lu - tion's here and you know it's right.

And you know that it's right. We have got to get it to-geth - er,

we have got to get it to-geth - er now.

Hand out the arms and am - mo we're gon - na

blast our way through here,_____ we got to get____ to - geth - er soon - er or lat -

See Emily Play

Words & Music by Syd Barrett

Sunshine Of Your Love

Words & Music by Jack Bruce, Pete Brown & Eric Clapton

be with you dar - ling soon, __ I'll be with you when __ the stars start fall - ing.

I've __ been wait - ing so __ long

to __ be where __ I'm go - ing, in __ the sun - shine of __ your

love. ___ *Fine* I'm with you my love,

A Whiter Shade Of Pale

Words & Music by Keith Reid & Gary Brooker

they the might wait just - er as brought well a be tray,___ closed,___ And so it

was___ that la - ter as the mil - ler told his

tale,___ that her face at first just ghost - ly, turned a

whit - er___ shade of pale.___ pale.___

Unchained Melody

Words by Hy Zaret. Music by Alex North

When Will I Be Loved?

Words & Music by Phil Everly

I've been made blue   I've been lied to

When will I be loved   I've been

turned down   I've been pushed 'round   When will I be

You'll Never Walk Alone

Music by Richard Rodgers. Words by Oscar Hammerstein II

With great warmth, like a hymn

When you walk through a storm, hold your head up high and don't be a-fraid of the dark. _____ At the

7/00 (37643)